WHAT I LOVE ABOUT GRANDPA

1

I’m really proud of

____.

2

You have taught me so much about

____.

3

I love to imagine you back when

____.

4

The world needs to know about your

____.

5

I love when you call me

"____."

6

It’s cool how you still

____.

7

When I was little, I loved

with you.

8

I love rummaging through your

____

for

____.

9

I love the sound of your

____.

10

I love how you

____

every day.

11

I love to play

____

with you.

12

I love to hear your stories about

____.

13

I love how much you enjoy

____.

14

I'd love to know your secret for

____.

15

I love how you always say,

"____."

16

I think you know more about

____

than anyone I've ever met.

17

I love watching

____

with you.

18

The story of your

____

would make a great movie.

19

You have great taste in

____.

20

I love remembering the time

you took me to

_______________________________________.

21

I so admire your

____.

22

You look extra-sharp when
you wear that

____.

23

I love how you never

____.

24

I love how you always

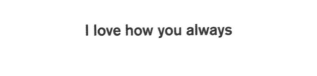

____.

25

If I had to describe you in one word, it'd be

____.

26

I love eating

____

with you.

27

The sound of

____

always reminds me of you.

28

If you were in charge of

____,

the world would be a

____

place.

29

I really value your advice about

____.

30

You make our family much more

____.

31

If you were a sport, you'd be

____.

32

I hope you get to

____

your favorite

____

soon.

33

Can I borrow your

sometime?

34

I love that you are much more

____

than most people would guess.

35

Thanks for helping me

____.

36

One of my favorite memories

is when

____.

37

Your philosophy of life is truly

________________________________.

38

Seeing you

____

always makes me smile.

39

I wonder if you know how much
our family appreciates your

______________________________________.

40

You

____

the best

____

ever.

41

If you were a musical instrument,

you'd be

____.

42

I love going to

____

with you.

43

I'd love to give you all the

____

you could ever want!

44

I have to admit you're usually right about

____.

45

You deserve the

____

award.

46

I still can't believe you

____

when you were

____.

47

I hope to be as

____

as you one day.

48

I always want to hear what
you're going to say about

______________________________.

49

I hope we can

____

together soon.

50

Thank you for being so

____.

I LOVE YOU, GRANDPA.

Fill in the *Love*®

Created, published, and distributed by Knock Knock
11111 Jefferson Blvd. #5167
Culver City, CA 90231
knockknockstuff.com
Knock Knock is a registered trademark of Knock Knock LLC
Fill in the Love is a registered trademark of Knock Knock LLC

ISBN: 978-168349049-4
UPC: 825703-50260-2
10 9

#fillinthelove